# MUSICAL INSTRUCTIONS

### Learning the Songs

The majority of the songs in this collection are folksongs that have been passed on orally, and have never before been written down. Keep this in mind when you train and perform them.

The quickest and best way of learning them is without notes! Listen first to the whole of the song on the tape. Explain the background to the song and its contents. After this read the text rhythmically from an overhead-projector or display. Then sing ahead of the others, voice for voice, phrase for phrase. Do not use a piano! With simpler songs the choir can be allowed itself to try and harmonize. The better the choir-leader knows the song, preferably without notes, the quicker and better can the choir learn it.

### The Songs are suitable for all choirs

These songs are perfectly suitable for singing in other ensembles than the traditional four-part choir (SATB). In a choir with only one male part, the alto can sing the tenor line (all of the tenor parts lie within the alto-register). Soprano 2 sings alto. Alternatively the bass line can be left out, and you can sing in three-part.

In a women's and men's choir the three highest parts (SSA/TTB) can be sung.

In a children's choir many of the songs can be sung either with the alto part as a second voice, or the tenor part (sounding an octave higher) as a descant.
For example: Melody and second voice: Freedom is coming, Singabahambayo, Bamthatha.
Melody and descant: Siph' amandla, Haleluya! Pelo tsa rona. Naturally all the songs can also be sung in a three-part children's choir in the same way as in a women's choir.

When you sing in the different groups, choose the key that is most suitable. These various combinations all sound well, and are not theoretical constructions, but rather just as the songs are often performed in South Africa.

So:

| Four-part mixed choir | Three-part mixed choir | | Women's choir | Men's choir | Children's choir | | |
|---|---|---|---|---|---|---|---|
| S | S1 | S | S1 | T1 | Melody | Melody | S1 |
| A | S2 | A | S2 | T2 | Second voice | – | S2 |
| T | A | Barytone | A | B | – | Descant | A |
| B | B | – | – | – | – | – | – |

### Movements

In South Africa these songs are performed almost without exception with some form of movement, often with a more, or less complicated "step", carried out by the whole choir together. To learn these movements to perfection is difficult, specially with a sheet of notes and a tape (!), but to sing these songs entirely without bodily expressions is just about impossible! The songs "demand" movement, something that feels unusual at first, but liberating later. It can be enough with a little "rocking" motion or a small step to and fro sideways so as to make the song "lift".

### Rhythm Instruments

The songs in this collection were originally in the language of Nguni (Zulu and Xhosa). The exception is "Haleluya! Pelo tsa rona," which is in Sotho. In contrast to many other African peoples, the drum has played a small role among the Nguni people, and today drums are used very seldom with choirs. All of the songs in the collection are normally performed wholly a capella, and can with advantage be so sung by us. This does not of course mean that it would be wrong, depending on means and interest, to have rhythm instruments as accompaniment. A number of suggestions for rhythm are given below.

## Text and Pronunciation

The English texts are, as far as possible, direct translations from the original in Zulu, Xhosa and Sotho. In some songs the English version has been expanded and developed so as to bring out more clearly the underlying conditions in South Africa.

Listen to the tape in order to make the pronunciation as accurate as possible.
"Th" is pronounced like t in "talk"
"Ph" is pronounced like p in "park"
"a" is pronounced like u in "under"
"e" is pronounced like a in "say", without the final sound we give it in English by slightly closing the mouth.
"i" is pronounced like i in "fit"
"o"is pronounced like o in "Tom"
"u" is pronounced like oo in "pool"

Other sounds that are more difficult to pronounce are explained in connection with the special instructions below.

## Form and funktion

These are freedom songs, both in form and function!

Many of these songs are more or less improvisations that have been taken down. In South Africa there are no two choirs that sing one and the same song alike, nor is there any choir that sings the same song alike twice in succession! Singing is an on-going creative process in which all the singers take part.

The important thing is not so much the song's form as its function. With the African way of telling a tale, it is impossible to "sing wrong". This is an inaccurate way of putting it. The essential thing is not how you sing, but that you mean what you sing and sing what you mean. It is impossible to sing a hymn without the whole body taking part in the words of praise, just as it is impossible to sing a freedom song without feeling the pain of the whole struggle.

It is also important to remember that African songs are collective in nature and that the boundaries between choir/listeners and choir/choir-leader are shifting and can even vanish. The song is born from the community.

Keep these attitudes in mind while working on the material!

Do not let the notes become an inhibiting factor in the creation of the music, but a point of departure!

Be free in your songs! Better a song with small musical defects that lives than a perfect song that lacks vitality! God has a rare gift of playing beautifully on poor fiddles.

Place the songs in their setting! It is here that the song book has the important function of conveying through pictures and commentaries the background to the songs. But it is also important to anchor the songs in our own experience and not use them as exotic curiosities, but as living hymns and powerful freedom songs in our own reality.

AMANDLA!

***Freedom is coming***     $\mathord{\downarrow}$   $\mathord{d}$ = c.90

Regard the beat as divided into 3+3+2 semiquavers (eigth notes). Practise the rhythm with hand-clapping, rhythm instruments or by reading each phrase of the text rhythmically (e.g. **Jennifer, Jennifer, Peter**).When the rhythm has been established, be free in the performance. Add rhythm instruments and simple dance-steps, improvise harmony, according to taste. Oh freedom!

***Asikhatali***     $\mathord{\downarrow}$ = c.80

***Gabi, Gabi***     $\mathord{\downarrow}$ = c.112

***Ipharadisi***     $\mathord{\downarrow}$ =c.120

# FREEDOM IS COMING

Songs of Protest and Praise from South Africa
for mixed choir
collected and edited by Anders Nyberg

**UTRYCK**

Fålhagsleden 8 A
S – 753 24 UPPSALA
Sweden

Skm ✠

Church of Sweden Mission
Postbox 297
S – 751 05 UPPSALA
Sweden

# Foreword

South Africa is one of the few countries in the world which is ruled by a declared Christian government. Christian nationalism is what they subscribe to. According to the former Prime Minister, Vorster, it is an ideology that most closely resembles nazism in Hitler's Germany and fascism in Mussolini's Italy. No-one who has studied the real situation in South Africa with open eyes has reason to doubt the Prime Minister's words. The white minority regime stops at no method to maintain and consolidate its power.

But out of the suffering of the Black People a song is born. The singer can be silenced, but never the song: the hope of a free country, the dream of freedom, this song can never be taken from the people.

It booms out from the court-room where the young people accused of treason sing their freedom-songs with raised fists.

It booms out from Pretoria Central Prison where those condemned to death sing day-in, day-out from their cells. The night before an execution there is never silence, and when dawn breaks the condemned man sings the song of his comrades during the last steps through the double-door to the gallows.

But above all else the South African song is a victory-song, a defiant hymn.

This song sounds out when two thousand women and children gather on a sandy field outside Capetown. They refuse to be separated from their menfolk and sent to Transkei, a "homeland" a thousand miles away, where starvation and sickness awaits them, a reserve that many have never been in, but which is now according to the apartheid policy the only legal domicile for these women. Despite constant harassment from the police, despite the cold and rain the women stand there round the fires and the wooden cross − and sing hymns. After six weeks of unbroken singing the patience of the police ends. Early one morning, just before dawn, they strike. Heavily armed and with dogs they occupy the small hills around the camp. The women gather round the cross, fall to their knees in the wet sand and pray. Then they dance round the cross, the symbol of this folly. These women have lost everything − their homes, their families, their jobs and their possessions. They have nothing more to lose − only their chains, but everything to win. Therefore they are filled with songs of praise. "Happy are you when people hate you,reject you, insult you, and say you are evil, all because of the Son of Man! Be glad when that happens, and dance for joy." The police they don't dance, and why should they? They have everything to lose and nothing to win. "But how terrible for you who are rich now; you have had your easy life! How terrible for you who are full now; you will go hungry! How terrible for you who laugh now; you will mourn and weep!" When the sun slowly rises over the mountain peaks, one of the women begins with "Akanamandla" and in triumph the crowd makes for the police-trucks to let themselves be arrested. "Akanamandla"− He has no power! Halleluya! Satan is powerless!

"Amandla" means power, and certainly their is power in these songs! The songs were published for the first time in Sweden in 1980 by the song group "Fjedur" and Church of Sweden Mission, after a visit made by the group to South Africa. Encouraged by the fantastic response the songs received in Scandinavia we would now like to make them available to English-speaking singers.

Our hope this time also is that the songs will give a true, liberating joy, but also engage us in the struggle for justice and peace in South Africa. Moreover we hope that these songs will get us to reflect on our own role in the world. We live ourselves in an apartheid situation where we as the rich, white minority live well by exploiting the poor, dark-skinned majority: the Third Word. It is just this confrontation which has become clearly focussed in South Africa, and has reached explosion point: underdeveloped versus developed countries, the exploitation of the poor by the rich. It is out of this struggle that these songs have been born, and it is that reality they describe.

If we can enter into these fantastic songs genuinely and fully, we will automatically be faced with many difficult and painful questions: Where do we stand in this struggle? Where does our society stand, our Church? Do we find ourselves among these crazy, singing women round the cross who lost everything but just because of this are open to receive God's Kingdom? Or do we find ourselves among the well-to-do who refuse to part with their privileges and positions, and just because of this will lose all? Where do we stand? Where does Jesus stand?

Our innermost hope with this material is this: that we by borrowing these songs of the poor and oppressed will gain a deeper understanding of the joyful message of the poor, of the liberating power of the Gospel, and that in this way we may be able to make these jubilant songs our own.

*Singabahambayo*    ♩ =c.110

*Siph' amandla*    ♩ =c.90

*Akanamandla*    ♩ =c.104

The soprano's rhythm can be practised frequently! Read S against A,T,B in the speaking choir. Use the pauses for a very active listening to the rhythm of the opposite group.

*Bamthatha*    ♩=c.78

*Vula Botha*    ♩=c.92

"Ngq" in "siyangqongqoza" (we knock) is a click-sound obtained by letting the tongue click against the palate — not unlike the sound of a cork being drawn out of a champagne bottle.

*Shumayela*    ♩ =c.60

*Nkosi, Nkosi*    ♩=c.52

The musical bow (see picture p.28) is a traditional instrument that is used as an accompaniment to song. With the Xhosa people these songs are often built up round two major chords with whole tone intervals. In "Nkosi, Nkosi", which is a recently composed song in this traditional style, the chords are F-major and G-major. Take care with the tone b in the middle voices (the third in G-major) that easily becomes too low. The letter c in "nenceba" is pronounced with a gentle smack with the tip of the tongue against the upper row of teeth. Listen to the tape. Suggestion for drum rhythm:

*Siyahamba*    ♩=c.102

*Haleluya! Pelo tsa rona*    ♩ c.126

A typical example of polyrhythm: "two to three" (3/4 beat to 6/8 beat).

Vary this basic rhythm in the drumming, hand-clapping, dance-steps, etc.

*Thuma mina*    ♩= c.58

This song lends itself for use in a service. The leader introduces the prayer, the congregation responds. The congregation can also, on the initiative of the leader, hum the verse while a prayer is being read aloud.

*We shall not give up the fight*    ♩= c.110

Originally from South Africa, this song came to Europe via Tanzania. On its way it lost the original text and has been changed and developed. Read the text rhythmically and see to it that all the consonants, pauses and syncopations come in their right places. The descant can be left out.

# FREEDOM IS COMING

Oh Freedom, Oh Freedom
Oh Freedom, Freedom is coming
Oh yes I know
Oh yes I know

Oh Jesus, Oh Jesus
Oh Jesus, Jesus is coming
Oh yes I know
Oh yes I know

# We are free
# and kept alive
# by hope

# ASIKHATALI

Asikhatali noma si boshwa
Sizimisel' inkululeko
Unzima lomthwalo
Ufuna madoda

It doesn't matter if you should jail us
We are free and kept alive by hope
our struggle's hard
But vict'ry will
Restore our lands
To our hands

I have no doubt that one day
we will all, black and white,
be free, for God made us freely
for freedom.
And nothing in the end can
frustrate God's purpose.
Bishop Desmond Tutu

# GABI, GABI

Gabi, Gabi
Bash' abazalwan'
Siyoshiywa khona
Sidal' ubuzalwan'

Praise the Father
Liberator Lord
He frees all the captives
And gives the hungry bread

No direct translation

13

Here on Mount Zion the Lord Almighty
will prepare a banquet for all the
nations of the world — a banquet of
the richest food and the finest wine.
Here he will suddenly remove the cloud
of sorrow that has been hanging over
the nations.
The Sovereign LORD will destroy death
for ever! He will wipe away the tears
from everyone's eyes and take away the
disgrace his people have suffered
throughout the world. The LORD himself
has spoken!
Isaiah 25.6—8

14

# IPHARADISI

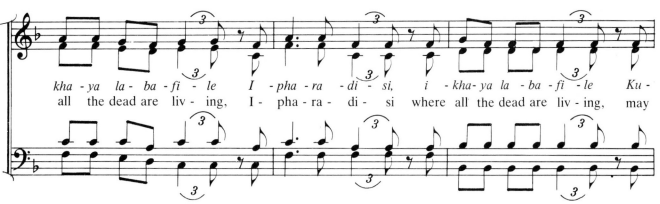

*Ipharadisi, ikhaya labafile*
*Kulapho sophumla khona*

Ipharadisi where all the dead are living
May we one day join them all there.

''*On earth an army is marchin,*

# SINGABAHAMBAYO

Singabahambayo thina
kulomhlaba
kepha sinekhaya
eZulwini
Sithi haleluya

On earth an army is marching
We're going home
Our longing bears a song
So sing out strong
Sithi Halleluya

With love our hearts are ablazing
For those who roam
And wander far away
Though longing home
Sithi Halleluya

Each day our friendship is growing
And with all speed
We share our wine and bread
A hasty meal
Sithi Halleluya

A few weeks ago one of the gunmen involved in the Silverton Raid* was buried in Soweto. 15.000 people attended the funeral − most of whom were young blacks. Their perceptions were quite different from those of most whites, who regarded the dead man as a terrorist − the blacks honoured him and his companions as heroes. I am sure those who attended the funeral knew they would have to run the gauntlet of squads of policemen; that they might have their eyes smarting from teargas, and that they might well have to escape the snapping jaws of vicious police dogs. And yet they came in their thousands, with clenched fists beating against the skies, and their throats pouring forth what we call our freedom songs. "God give us strength, give us strength not to fear, give us strength because we need it" − Siph' amandla Nkosi'!
Bishop Desmond Tutu

*The Silverton raid was an ANC operation − an attack on a bank − that developed into a siege during which three ANC men were killed.

# SIPH' AMANDLA

Siph' amandla Nkosi
Wokungesabi
Siph' amandla Nkosi
Siyawadinga

O God give us power
To rip down prisons
O God give us power
To lift the people

O God give us courage
To withstand hatred
O God give us courage
Not to be bitter

O God give us power
And make us fearless
O God give us power
Because we need it

"He has
no power"

karin st. '83

20

# AKANAMANDLA

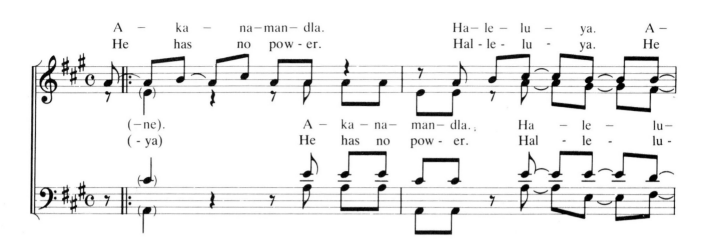

| | |
|---|---|
| Akanamandla | He has no power |
| Haleluya | Halleluya |
| Akanamandla | He has no power |
| USathane | Satan's had it! |
| | |
| Simdumazile | He has been cheated |
| Haleluya | Halleluya |
| Simdumazile | He has been cheated |
| USathane | Satan's had it! |
| | |
| Simsabisile | He flees far from us |
| Haleluya | Halleluya |
| Simsabisile | He flees far from us |
| USathane | Satan's had it! |

Winnie Mandela

I visited one of these banned people, Winnie Mandela. Her husband, Nelson Mandela, is serving a life sentence on Robben Island, our maximum security prison. I wanted to take her Holy Communion. The police told me I couldn't enter the house. So we celebrated Holy Communion in my car in the street in Christian South Africa. On a second occasion I went to see her on a weekend. Her restriction order is more strict at weekends. She can't leave her yard. So we celebrated Holy Communion again in the street. This time Winnie was on one side of the fence and I on the other. This in Christian South Africa in 1978.

Bishop Desmond Tutu

# BAMTHATHA

Bamthatha
Bambeka eIsland
Wasuka wakhala
wathi "amandla"

He's locked up
Sent to Robben Island
We shall never sorrow:
Power to the people

Kawuthethe
Thetha Winnie, thetha
Thetha Winnie, thetha
Khulul' isizwe

Speak out loud
Speak out, Winnie, speak out
Speak out to the people:
Freedom to our land

23

# HE HAS CHOSEN ME

to bring good news to the poor.
He has sent me to proclaim liberty
to the captives
and recovery of sight to the blind;
to set free the oppressed
and announce that the time has come
when the Lord will save his people.
Luke 4.18 — 19

# VULA BOTHA

| Vula Botha | Open Botha |
|---|---|
| *siyangqongqoza* | We are a'knocking |
| *Khulul' uMandela* | Release Mandela |
| *Asikhokhele* | our leader |

# SHUMAYELA

*Shumayela ivangeli !*
*Mali hambe ivangeli !*

Come let us preach the Gospel

*"Lord have mercy"*

# NKOSI, NKOSI

Music by G. M. Kolisi

Nko-si, Nko—si, yi–ba nen–ce–ba.

Kres–tu, Kres–tu, yi–ba nen–ce–ba.

Lord have mer–cy, have mer–cy up–on us

Christ have mer–cy, have mer–cy up–on us

Nkosi, Nkosi, yiba nenceba
Krestu, Krestu, yiba nenceba

Lord have mercy, have mercy upon us
Christ have mercy, have mercy upon us

# SIYAHAMBA

Siyahamb' ekukhanyen' kwenkhos'.

We are marching in the light of God.

*"All our hearts
are filled with gladness"*

# HALELUYA! PELO TSA RONA

Haleluya! Pelo tsa rona
Di thabile kaofela

Ke Morena Jeso
Ya re dumeletseng
Ya re dumeletseng
Ho tsamaisa evangedi

O na na le bo mang?
Le barutuwa ba hae
O na na le bo mang?
Le barutuwa ba hae

Halleluya! We sing your praises
All our hearts are filled with gladness

Christ the Lord to us said:
I am wine, I am bread
I am wine, I am bread
Give to all who thirst and hunger

Now he sends us all out
Strong in faith free of doubt
Strong in faith free of doubt
Tell all men the joyful Gospel

# THUMA MINA

*Thuma mina Somandla*
*Roma nna Modimo*

Send me Jesus, send me Lord
Lead me Jesus . . .
Fill me Jesus . . .

# WE SHALL NOT GIVE UP THE FIGHT

1. We shall not give up the fight. We have on - ly start - ed, we have on - ly start - ed, we

have on - ly start - ed. We shall not give up the fight. We have on - ly start - ed, we

have on - ly start - ed, we have on - ly start - ed. 2. To - geth - er we'll have vic - to - ry, hand
3. Nev - er, ev - er put to flight, we're

hold - ing hand, hand hold - ing hand, hand hold - ing hand. To -
bound to win, we're bound to win, we are bound to win.

geth - er we'll have vic-to-ry, hand hold - ing hand, hand hold - ing hand, hand
Nev - er ev - er put to flight, we're bound to win, we're bound to win, we

# Contents